Plastering &
Rendering

KIM KENNERSON

MINI·WORKBOOK·SERIES

MURDOCH
B O O K S

CONTENTS

A wall plastered in the traditional manner (top), applying render (far left) and installing plasterboard (left)

Cement render provides a neat and attractive finish for a wall, and it can be used to camouflage the use of different materials in construction. Including coloured oxides in the mix makes painting unnecessary.

Mortar mixes

Cement rendering is used for both interior and exterior work, although the ratios of the mortar mixes will vary according to the use. Selecting the appropriate mix is essential for a good job.

MORTAR MIXES

The mortar mix used for a job will determine the quality of the work. When selecting a mix, consider whether the wall is outside or inside, and the condition of the background. Never use a strong mortar on a weak background, for instance a mortar coat that contains less cement than the final coat. As the mortar dries and shrinks it will exert stress on the background, resulting in the mortar lifting away from the background.

FOR EXTERIOR WORK

Cement mortar is used for rendering exterior walls, as it is strong enough to stand up to varying weather conditions and is water-resistant. An ideal mix is three parts good-quality clean sand (plasterers' sharp sand) and one part Portland cement (3:1).

FOR INTERIOR WORK

For interior work composition mortar (mortar that contains lime) is suitable. This mortar may be used as a one-coat cement render finish or as a base coat for plastering. A suitable mix is nine parts plasterers' sharp sand, two parts Portland cement and one part lime (9:2:1), but ratios can vary and it is not unusual for a ratio of 6:2:1 to be employed, for instance, if the sand is of poor quality.

MIXING MORTAR

Mix the materials together thoroughly, make a well in the centre and add water a little at a time. When it is ready, the mortar should retain its shape. Mix small amounts using a gauging trowel in a bucket or on a mortar board. For large jobs use a wheelbarrow and a shovel, or a cement mixer.

MORTAR BOARD AND STAND

You can make a mortar board from a piece of board 12–18 mm thick and about 1 m square.

Rest the mortar board on a stand at a comfortable height while you are mixing the mortar.

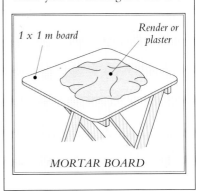

1 x 1 m board

Render or plaster

MORTAR BOARD

Applying render

Rendering is not difficult, and you can achieve a satisfactory result as long as the background is well prepared and you have practised the basic application skills.

PREPARING THE BACKGROUND

Before you start cement rendering, you must prepare the background (or base) well to ensure the render will bond to the surface and not fall off. The preparation necessary will vary according to the weather and site conditions, the time of the year and the condition of the base. The ideal background is a wall of dry-pressed common bricks. However, extruded clay bricks or concrete blocks present no special problems if they are dry and clean. The following method will ensure most backgrounds are ready for rendering.

1 Remove any materials that may interfere with the rendering. These may include protruding mortar and crumbling mortar that was used to fill grooves where plumbing and electrical conduits have previously been inserted.

2 Using a stiff bristle brush or wire brush, clean down the wall to remove any dirt, dust, efflorescence salts or other foreign material.

3 Cover any aluminium on the wall, such as window frames, as mortar can

TOOLS AND MATERIALS

- Scutch hammer
- Stiff bristle brush or wire brush
- Hose
- Bucket, mortar board or wheelbarrow
- Cement or composition mortar
- Pointing trowel
- Plasterers' trowel
- Plasterers' hawk
- Wooden float
- Sponge float
- Aluminium or timber straight edge
- Spirit level
- Water brush
- Scratcher
- Steel squares and measuring gauge
- Hooks or holdfast pins
- Angle tool
- Measuring tape

stain aluminium if it comes in contact with it.

4 If the background is smooth concrete, clean it thoroughly and roughen it or flick on mortar made of two parts coarse sand and one part Portland cement to provide a better key for the render.

Red and yellow oxides were added to this cement render as it was mixed on the mortar board. Mortar was then placed on the plasterers hawk so that it could be easily transferred to the trowel and applied to the wall.

5 Splash some water onto the wall to judge how strong the suction is. If water stays on the surface, use a brush to splash a small amount of water over the wall. If suction is strong, hose down the wall liberally from the top, allowing water to flow over the surface. Water controls the suction, ensuring better bonding, and assists in curing the applied mortar.

APPLYING RENDER

Cement render may be applied in one, two or even three coats according to the background and the type of finish required. However, the one-coat method described here is most commonly used.

Corners are rendered at the same time as the walls. Render one wall, followed by the corner and then the other wall. Any corner requires special attention, whether it is between a wall and ceiling, at a door or window opening or on an engaged pier. The precise procedures vary, but there are basic guidelines that will cover most situations (see steps 15–19 on pages 9 and 10). The finished work needs to be vertical, level, straight and square, with good shape and finish.

6 Mix the appropriate mortar (see page 5). At the top of the wall, or at a convenient height, use a plasterers' trowel to apply a narrow, horizontal band of mortar (a screed) slightly thicker than the finished thickness of 10–12 mm.

7 Apply a second horizontal screed of mortar near the bottom of the wall, about 100 mm from the floor. This makes it easier to rule off and will allow you to shovel up dropped mortar without damaging the wall.

8 Hold a timber or aluminium straight edge vertically at one end of the wall. Using a spirit level to ensure it is vertical, rub the straight edge into the screeds. The marks made in the screeds (known as dots) indicate the finished plane of the wall. Repeat at the other end.

9 Use the straight edge to rule the rest of the screeds down to the level of the dots. To rule the screeds down, move the straight edge up and down slightly while moving it horizontally along the wall.

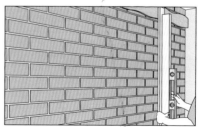

8 To check that the screeds are aligned, place a spirit level on the straight edge and ensure it is vertical.

HINT

When taking a rule or straight edge away from a corner, slide it gently along the wall, away from the corner.

10 Place the mortar on the plasterers' hawk. Use a plasterers' trowel to fill in the area between the screeds, working top to bottom and right to left for a right-handed person (in the opposite direction for a left-hander). Apply the mortar evenly, just a little thicker than the final coat.

11 Allow the mortar to dry a little and then rule it off to the now hardened screeds. Fill in hollows and rule off again until only very small holes and irregularities are left.

12 Use a water brush to splash water on the surface and then work over it with a wooden float until it is even. Don't overwet the surface.

13 To produce a finer finish, use a sponge float as the final tool, rubbing the face of the wall lightly in a circular motion and adding a little splash of water if necessary. Use an angle tool to finish internal corners.

14 Clean mortar from surrounding timber or aluminium frames while it is still wet, by scraping it off or using a brush or sponge.

RENDERING AN EXTERNAL CORNER

15 After rendering one wall, you can render the corner. If you are rendering onto dried mortar, dampen the mortar to avoid applying new mortar against a dry face.

16 Secure a straight edge on the corner, on the already rendered face. Use a spirit level to ensure it is straight and vertical, and hold it in place with hooks or cramps, or have a helper hold it. You can try holding it with your left hand while you work with the right hand, but you will find this awkward.

17 Render the other face of the wall in the normal manner, working

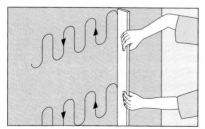

11 Allow the mortar to dry a little and then rule it off to the now hardened screeds.

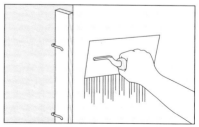

17 Render the other face of the wall in the normal manner, working towards the corner.

towards the corner and applying a little more than the estimated final thickness of mortar.

18 Rule off and work with a wooden float to the straight edge. When ruling off mortar from corners, always work backwards away from the corner, as this helps prevent the mortar being loosened. Use a steel square to check the corner.

19 Remove the straight edge and finish the corner (see the box on the opposite page).

RENDERING ATTACHED PIERS

1 Render the walls on either side of the pier, working as described on pages 8–9.

2 Place vertical straight edges against either side of the pier, in line with the face, and hold them in place with hooks or holdfast pins. Apply render to the face of the pier.

3 Place a vertical straight edge against the face and use a steel square to

---

HINT

• When rendering openings, always use a hand float long enough to span across the area being rendered, as this minimizes hollows in the work and you will achieve a better finish.

• Use a measuring gauge to maintain equal widths on sills and heads, and use a steel square to check internal and external corners for square.

---

check for square. Then apply mortar to the side of the pier and allow it to firm. Scrape back excess mortar using a steel square laid against the straight edge and back wall. Float the side of the pier.

4 Reposition the straight edge on the opposite side of the pier and use a spirit level to ensure that it is vertical. Measure at the top, bottom and in the middle to check that both sides of the pier are parallel and vertical. Apply mortar to the second side of the pier as in step 3.

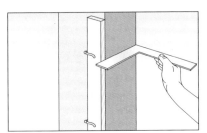

3 Scrape back excess mortar using a steel square laid against the straight edge and the back wall.

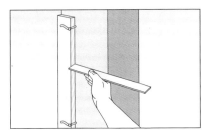

4 Measure at the top, bottom and in the middle to check that both sides of the pier are parallel and vertical.

FINISHING A CORNER

The precise shape of a corner can vary, from a sharp right-angle to a gentle curve or bevel. A round finish will be less subject to chipping than a square finish and so is used in areas of hard wear and frequent traffic.

PENCIL ROUND

A pencil round is the most commonly used finish, so-called because it is similar in shape to a round lead pencil. To produce this finish, use a long, narrow wooden float (450 mm is best) to slightly dull and splay the arris (the sharp corner), then work the float back and forth around the corner, approximately to the desired shape. Finish the shape by running a metal angle tool vertically up and down the corner.

SQUARE ARRIS

A square arris is a sharp, right-angled corner. It is mainly used where damage is unlikely to occur, such as on window and door heads, or on ceiling beams. Use an angle tool to produce it.

DULLED ARRIS

The sharp corner is bevelled to produce a dulled arris. It is mostly used on piers and in light traffic areas where corners are not likely to be damaged. It may be employed as a decorative feature.

SPLAYED ARRIS

Similar to a dulled arris, a splayed arris has a wider chamfer or bevelled edge. It is a decorative finish and is also suitable for use in areas at high risk of damage such as passageways and living rooms.

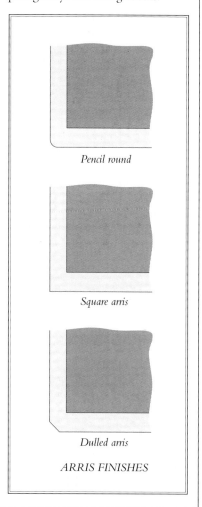

Pencil round

Square arris

Dulled arris

ARRIS FINISHES

Repairing render

Holes or cracks in render can be repaired, although the repair may be visible as it is usually difficult to match the texture of the original render.

POTENTIAL PROBLEMS

Problems with cement render work will usually show up within about eighteen months of completing the work. Render may crack and fall from the wall, or areas may lift away from the wall. These drummy areas will give a hollow sound if you tap them with your knuckles or run a coin over the surface.

Render may fail for a number of reasons, many relating to the original rendering work.

- The mortar dried out too quickly.
- The render is not adhering properly, as the background was incorrectly prepared.
- The mortar is stronger than the base so that it lifts or pulls away from the base.
- There was excessive shrinkage as the mortar mix was too strong.
- The walls were too dry or too wet when the render was applied.
- Poor-quality materials were used for the mortar.
- Unsuitable ratios of materials were used in the mortar.
- Incorrect techniques were used to apply the mortar.
- There has been some vibration or hammering close to the wall, or building movement.
- Too many additives were used in the mortar.

PATCHING CEMENT RENDER

1 Mix a batch of mortar (see page 5 for a suitable mix).

2 Determine the extent of the area that needs to be patched, and remove the faulty render using a scutch hammer or a hammer and chisel. Wear safety glasses and a mask.

3 Apply a sealant solution of 1 part PVA to 5 parts water to the exposed surface. This will help to bond the new render to the masonry.

4 Mix some mortar, adding a little liquid plasticizer to help workability. Apply mortar to the area to be patched, slightly overfilling the hole.

5 When the mortar has firmed up, use a straight length of timber to scrape it back to the level of the surrounding surface.

6 Use a hand float to work over the surface of the patch until you have an even finish and the patched area is flush with the surrounding surface.

A crack in render caused by structural movement (left), and a patch where render has fallen from a badly prepared wall (right) are common problems.

Sponge-float the patch so that it matches the surrounding area.

7 Clean the surrounding area, checking that the patched surface is flush and matches the original surface as closely as possible.

FIXING VERTICAL CRACKS

Cracks may appear in render where different construction materials meet, for example brickwork and a concrete pier, as different materials have different rates of movement.

It is impossible to prevent this type of crack, and so the best treatment is to provide a joint where the cracking is likely to occur. In this way the cracking is confined to the joint and so is less noticeable. In effect, you are creating an expansion joint in the render.

CREATING A JOINT IN HARD RENDER

If there is a crack in existing render and it is relatively straight you can create a joint in the hard render.

Place a timber or aluminium straight edge against the crack and use a spirit level to check it is vertical. Take a masonry cutting disc (used with an angle grinder), cut it in half and run the edge of the disc up and down against the rule until you have made a deep and even joint through the thickness of the render. It is much quicker to use an angle grinder, but it is more difficult to produce a neat, straight line with it.

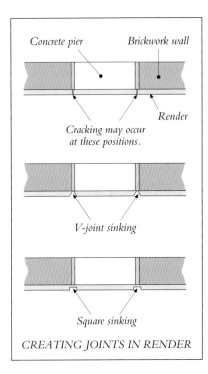

Concrete pier   Brickwork wall

Render

Cracking may occur
at these positions.

V-joint sinking

Square sinking

CREATING JOINTS IN RENDER

CREATING A JOINT IN FRESH RENDER

To make a joint in fresh render, draw a line in the render where the background materials join, position a straight edge as a guide and use a metal template or V-jointing tool to form a joint. Alternatively, a square sinking can be produced, also with a metal template.

You can also use construction mastic, bitumen, foam-type products or metal beadings to make a joint.

USING PREFABRICATED EXPANSION JOINTS

Where there is an existing expansion joint in a wall, the render must also be treated in such a way as to allow expansion. Prefabricated metal expansion joints are available, and they can be used to hide or form a joint. They are set into position before rendering.

Place the metal strip accurately over the existing expansion joint. Use masonry nails to fix it to the brickwork or background. Apply render up to or over the metal strip, finishing flush with the upper edge of the strip. Then use brushes or rags to thoroughly clean the metal strip (metal tools should not be used, as they may scratch the metal).

RANDOM CRACKS

Less regular cracks will appear in render where there is structural movement or other disturbance, for example where plumbing or an electrical conduit has been installed and the groove has been filled with poor-quality mortar.

These cracks are repaired in the same way as cracks in plaster (see page 35). Finish the new render as usual and ensure the repaired area is flush with the surrounds.

PAINTING FRESH RENDER

If you want to paint rendered surfaces, first allow the render to dry thoroughly. Then apply a coat of sealer, following the manufacturer's instructions. Again, allow it to dry and then proceed with an undercoat and finishing coats of paint.

COLOURING RENDER

To produce quality coloured render you should apply two coats, a first coat of ordinary cement mortar and a finishing coat that includes the colour. Colours can be added to lime mortars, although fading will result with certain products.

The sand and cement you use will also affect the colour of the render. To produce white render, use a white sand and white or off-white Portland cement, which is made from white limestone and white clay.

These lighter cements are also used in coloured work to produce brighter and more vivid colours than are achieved with normal cement. The addition of yellow sand to yellow or red work will also increase the intensity of colour.

PIGMENTS

Coloured render is produced by adding pigments to the cement. Factory-prepared pigments are usually the best, as they are more uniformly mixed and ground. The most common colours available are red, brown, yellow, black and green. They are obtainable in the form of mineral oxides. The finer these powdered oxides are ground, the better they are.

Red, brown, yellow and black colours are obtained from oxide of iron, and black pigment is also obtained from oxide of manganese.

Green pigment is prepared from chromium oxide.

USING POWDERED OXIDES

When mixing dry oxides with cement, you should weigh and measure the neat cement and oxide very carefully, and mix them together in a dry state. Then sieve the material through a very fine mesh three or four times.

The amount of oxide required depends on the quality of the pigment and the drying conditions, as well as the depth of finished colour desired. The best way of determining the quantity to use is to make a small trial batch. Usually you will find that between 6 and 10 per cent of colour to neat cement is appropriate.

USING LIQUID COLOURS

Powdered dry oxides can be difficult to mix thoroughly through mortar and may result in streaking. They can be replaced by liquid colours, which have the advantages of being pre-mixed and readily absorbed by the mortar. By using liquid colours it is easy to maintain the same ratio and uniformity of colour in the mix.

Some liquid colours may, however, have the effect of 'killing' the plasticity of the mix, and in that case you will need to incorporate a plasticizer additive.

Walls sponged with ochre-coloured render are increasingly popular. The bagging can be kept neat to show the regular pattern of the underlying bricks or applied more liberally to achieve an informal effect.

Sponging

Sponging was originally used to fill holes and provide a rough texture to render. It is suitable for both internal and external applications, and the mortar can be coloured for extra effect.

THE TECHNIQUE

Traditionally, the mortar was spread over rough brickwork and rubbed over with a hessian bag, hence the old term 'bagging'. The technique has once again become popular, but plastic sponges and not hessian are now most commonly used to produce the effect. Almost any soft material, however, can be used to spread the mortar.

There are two ways to apply sponging to a wall.

METHOD 1

1 Prepare a mix of mortar in a wheelbarrow (see page 5), adding extra water to make a slurry. Add colouring to the mix if desired (see the box on page 15).

2 Dip a broom or brush into the slurry and apply a light smear of slurry to the wall. Use only a small amount at a time.

3 Spread the slurry over the surface using a plastic sponge, hessian bag or other soft material.

METHOD 2

1 Mix a suitable mortar (see page 5) in a wheelbarrow or on a mortar board. Add colouring to the mix if desired (see page 15).

2 Using a plasterers' hawk and trowel, spread a coat of mortar roughly over the wall to a thickness of no more than 5 mm (see pages 8–10). Depending on the finish required, you can leave the mortar rough or even it out.

3 Allow the mortar to firm up with background suction, but do not let it begin to dry.

4 Using a plastic sponge, work over the surface with a circular motion until you achieve your desired result, occasionally wetting the surface to keep the mortar workable. Wear gloves to protect your skin from the harsh materials.

4 Wearing gloves and using a plastic sponge, work over the surface with a circular motion.

Textured finishes

A wide variety of textured finishes are used on render, some achieved by applying mortar to the wall in special ways and some by working on applied mortar.

APPLYING TEXTURED FINISHES

Although a neat rendered wall is sufficient for most purposes, there may be occasions when you want to add a decorative texture. Combing, brush textures and even simulated stonework and brickwork can be achieved by a home handyperson with care and attention to detail. The applied aggregate finishes are usually produced by professionals, but you may need to patch a small area.

COMB EFFECTS

A toothed metal template or comb can be used to comb a still-soft rendered surface to produce a variety of textured finishes. Combing may be done vertically or horizontally. Basketweave, herringbone and zig-zag patterns are also popular.

BRUSH TEXTURES

To produce brush textures, begin with a straight, flat background of cement render or fibre cement sheeting. Apply a fresh coat of mortar and use a brush to make a pattern. A stiff, rounded sisal brush can be twisted against the soft mortar to produce random scroll effects, or the brush can be dabbed on or used to flick or splash on slurry.

SIMULATED BRICKWORK

Any type of brickwork can be imitated using coloured mortars and two-coat work. Decide on the brick bond you want to reproduce, and the colour for the 'mortar' (first coat) and 'bricks' (top coat). Apply the first coat and let it dry. Then apply the top coat and, with a straight edge and pencil, mark out the bricks. Use a

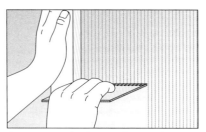

Use a toothed metal template to produce a variety of combed patterns in still soft mortar.

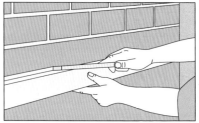

Using a straight edge and raking jointer, draw in the joints to produce simulated brickwork.

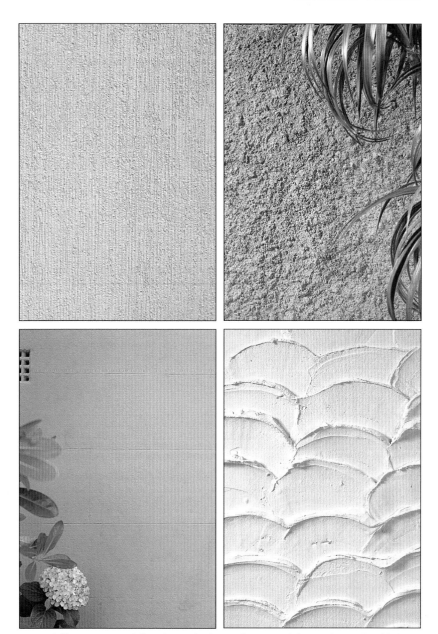

Four different textured finishes. Clockwise from top left: render with added grit over which a plastic foam float has been dragged; roughcast rendering; Spanish or fan effect; and simulated stonework.

ASHLAR STONEWORK

raking jointer or small piece of board to draw in the brick joints.

IMITATION STONEWORK

Stonework can be imitated very successfully with coloured mortar. A sandstone effect can be achieved simply by using a bright yellow sand and off-white cement, but the addition of a small amount of yellow oxide may enhance the effect.

For a natural-looking result, use a similar pattern of stonework on either side of an opening and align a horizontal joint with the top of any openings. If you are imitating an arch, the keystone must be centrally placed over the opening and should not be too large.

Coloured joints can be produced by applying a coloured mortar base and making the final coat (the 'stone') a different colour. When the joints are drawn in, the base colour will be exposed.

1 Decide on the type of blocks you want, for example ashlar (regular, rectangular blocks), random rubble or random flat blocks. Regular blockwork is sized to suit the wall size but is usually 300–450 mm high and 600–750 mm long.

2 Apply a coat of mortar to the background, finishing it with a timber float to give a sand-like effect.

3 Use a straight edge and pencil to mark out the joints and then draw them in with a raking jointer or other metal tool and straight edge.

4 Refine the surface of the 'blocks' by prodding with a wet sisal brush to give a sponge-like finish. Alternatively, you can lightly dab the stone face with a wire or stiff, rough brush, or a piece of rock or brick.

ROUGHCAST

Roughcast, also known as wet or spatter dash, is achieved by throwing a wet mixture onto a prepared background. This finish was often used on gable ends and walls of twentieth-century cottages but can also be used on internal walls. The aggregate provides texture to the finished wall but it is covered with the mortar.

You can achieve many different effects by including different stones and colour additives, or by using contrast colours in the background, off-white cement instead of grey or a different type of sand. The finish is also determined by the force of application, the consistency of the mix and the distance you stand from the wall when working.

It can be an advantage to practise on a test piece of board so that you achieve the results that please you most. Wear protective clothing and safety glasses during the work and protect surrounding areas. Use drop sheets to catch dropped mortar and gather it up frequently so you don't tread it in.

1 Render the background using composition mortar (see page 5), or nail or screw fibre cement sheeting to a timber or metal frame.

2 In a bucket prepare a mixture of four parts medium aggregate (fine stone or ash), two parts fine aggregate (clean sand) and one part Portland cement. Add 10 per cent lime and some water. Lime is added for extra plasticity and to help the mix retain water. Colour can be added if desired (see the box on colouring render on page 15). The mix should have a fairly wet consistency. Stir the mix well to prevent the materials separating.

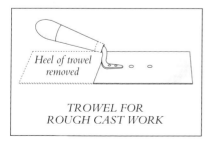

Heel of trowel removed

TROWEL FOR ROUGH CAST WORK

3 Begin work at the top of the wall, usually on the right-hand side. Hold the bucket under your left arm, against your body and at an inclination of 45 degrees from the horizontal. Scoop the mix out of the bucket with a trowel that has had the heel removed (see the diagram below left) and throw the mix on the wall in a flicking fashion, with the trowel turned so that its full width is towards the wall as the material is flicked on. Work with quick movements and vary the direction of the throw continually to prevent a streaky appearance. Avoid creating joins in the work.

4 Wash off any soiled surfaces as soon as possible. When the material firms up, you can flatten the high spots with a steel trowel or wooden float if you prefer.

PEBBLE DASH
Pebble dash (also called dry dash) is a finish achieved by applying coloured stones to a soft base, that is, dry material is added to a wet background, the reverse of roughcast. The pebbles will be exposed on the finished wall, so use pebbles that are all the same colour to avoid a patchy appearance. As you work, catch any falling stones with a drop sheet as they can then be reused.

1 Mix composition mortar (see page 5) and apply a coat of render (see pages 8–10) to the surface. Ensure it is straight.

2 Mix a wet mortar of five parts sand, one part cement and one and a half parts lime (5:1:1½), and use a trowel to spread it over the rendered wall to a thickness of about 10 mm.

3 While the mortar is still soft, flick on coloured stones or marble chips. Work with quick movements and vary the direction of the throw continually to prevent a streaky appearance. Avoid creating joins in the work. Do not press the stones into the mortar, as this will distort the shape. Instead, rely on the force of the throw to make the pebbles or chips adhere.

TYROLEAN SPRAY
A hand-held mechanical device known as a Tyrolean machine or gun can be used to produce a variety of textured finishes. As there is no aggregate in the mix used, the texture is much finer than that produced by rough cast work. The machine may be available from your local hardware store or plastering supply company, or you can hire one from a building equipment hire firm.

Tyrolean spray can be applied to brick, concrete, fibre cement sheeting and rendered backgrounds. The spray can be varied from light to heavy by adjusting the tension of the flat metal blades, which flick the material from within the container onto the wall, by means of a lever fitted to a tension bar. To work the gun, you rotate an external handle that drives a central shaft.

1 Prepare a slurry of about two and a half parts sand and two parts cement, and water to suit. Fine coats are produced by very wet mixes and heavy coats by a thicker mix. Keep the ratio of materials, and the amount of colour additive and water, exactly the same for each mix.

2 Stand the Tyrolean machine upright and pour in the slurry. Mix the mortar to an even paste by releasing the tension and winding the handle backwards. Adjust the tension to suit the effect required (usually a strong tension for the first, light coat). Practise on a test board before starting work on the wall.

3 To apply the first, light coat to the wall, stand directly facing the wall. Gradually walk the length of the wall, spraying the coat evenly over the surface, and allow it to dry slightly. Don't stop, or you will apply too much in one spot and the mortar will run down the wall.

4 If further coats are required, adjust the tension so that it is a little weaker

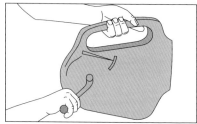

2 Mix the mortar to an even paste by releasing the tension and winding the handle backwards.

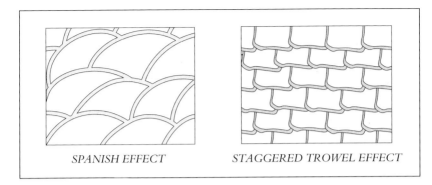

SPANISH EFFECT   *STAGGERED TROWEL EFFECT*

and stand at an angle of 45 degrees to the wall. Continue until the base is covered and the texture achieved.

5 If desired, you can flatten high spots on the surface with a steel trowel or wooden float.

SPANISH EFFECT

Also known as fan texture because of the shape of the pattern, Spanish effect has a heavy, rustic appearance. Use a plasterers' trowel to create a large pattern or a pointing trowel for a smaller pattern.

The mix ratio should be about five parts sand, one part cement and one and a half parts lime (5:1:1½). The extra lime produces a fatty mortar that is easy to apply and holds its shape. Painting these patterns is difficult, so use coloured mortar.

1 Provide a straight, flat surface for the background.

2 Apply mortar to the toe (front) end of the trowel and then place the heel (back) end of the trowel against the wall. Start at the top left-hand side of the wall. While applying pressure on the heel of the trowel, twist and force the trowel to left or right to produce the fan effect.

3 Add the second trowel full of mortar in line with and adjacent to the first 'fan'. Continue working from left to right and from top to bottom of the wall: random patterns are not as effective. Don't change operators because you need consistent hand pressure to produce an even and regular pattern.

STAGGERED TROWEL EFFECT

Staggered trowel effect is a variation on Spanish effect produced by applying separate trowels of mortar.

To achieve this effect, load mortar onto the full length of the trowel and apply it horizontally, commencing at the bottom of the wall. As the roll of mortar forms on the wall, increase pressure on the trowel so the mortar tapers off. Start at the bottom of the wall, apply one row and then the row above it, staggering each one.

Plastered walls make an excellent base for paint or wallpaper as they are completely smooth. Here, the external corner is finished with a staff bead to provide a neat finish and protection against damage.

Plaster

Plaster is a gypsum-based product for internal use on walls and ceilings. It provides a fine, smooth finish and was traditionally used for finishing walls in masonry buildings.

GYPSUM PLASTER

Plaster of Paris is the common name for gypsum plaster. It is produced by quarrying gypsum rock and then calcining or burning it so that it forms a powder. The plaster is then screened for fineness and, finally, packed. When mixed with water, plaster powder converts back to a material that is chemically similar to the original mineral rock from which it was derived.

USES

Plaster was traditionally used for finishing coats on internal walls and ceilings. It is used over a lime-based or cement-based rendering coat. Plaster is also used for patching, as a binder with other materials, and for casting ornate plaster mouldings such as cornices or ceiling roses. As it is made from rock, plaster is a fire-resistant material.

Gypsum plaster comes in a number of different forms (see the table below). Hardwall (or hard finish) and casting plasters are the most commonly used for modern plastering. When purchased, some types contain additives that will affect the quality of the plaster, slowing or hastening the setting time. Choose one to suit your job.

Gypsum plaster is available at hardware stores or speciality plaster stores in bags of various sizes. The bags should be stored in a dry place and protected from weather. Opened bags must be sealed tight.

Gypsum plaster is also used to make fibrous plaster sheets and plasterboard, which are used for dry-lining interior walls and ceilings.

TYPES OF GYPSUM PLASTER		
NAME	USE	APPROXIMATE SETTING TIME
Hardwall/hard finish	Walls and ceilings	1½ hours
Casting	Moulded products	4–6 minutes
Superfine	Plasterglass sheet	20–30 minutes
Dental	Dental products	15 minutes
Retarded	Spray plastering	3–4 hours

Applying plaster

A plaster finishing coat provides a smooth, medium-to-hard finish for interior walls. It is worthwhile following the correct procedures so that you achieve a good finish.

TRADITIONAL PLASTERING

There are two forms of traditional plastering: the three-coat system and the two-coat system. The three-coat system consists of a base coat and a floating coat (both cement based) and the plaster finishing coat. In the two-coat system the base coat is omitted. See the box on page 29 for another two-coat option.

The base coat is used to seal the surface, and then the floating coat is applied to the base to straighten it and provide a flat area on which to apply the plaster finishing coat. Without the floating coat very few bases will provide even suction, and as the finishing coat is only 3–4 mm thick, it will crack open if it shrinks.

PREPARING THE WALL

Correct preparation of the wall (the background) is essential to ensure successful plastering work. Poor preparation will often lead to faulty results. The type of preparation necessary will depend on the composition of the wall.

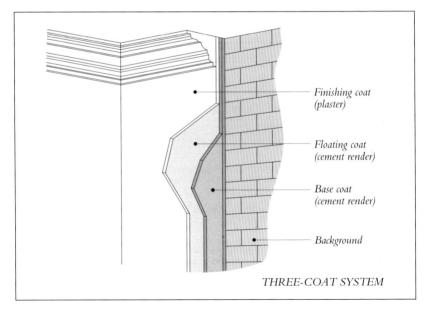

Finishing coat
(plaster)

Floating coat
(cement render)

Base coat
(cement render)

Background

THREE-COAT SYSTEM

Plaster is applied with a straight trowel, usually referred to as a plasterers trowel. Right-handed people start work at the bottom left-hand part of the wall, applying the plaster and roughly smoothing it out.

TOOLS AND MATERIALS

- Metal scratcher or comb
- Broom or brush
- Hardwall or hard finish plaster
- Plastering hydrated lime
- Mixing buckets
- Mortar board and stand
- Plasterers' trowel
- Pointing trowel
- Wooden float, about 450 mm long
- Plasterers' hawk
- Paintbrushes with fine, hair bristles
- Angle tool
- Metal corner beads

• Brick, block, concrete or stone walls should ideally be rendered with either lime mortar or composition mortar (see page 5). A rendered base will provide even suction and a hard base. The render should be wet down and lightly scratched to provide a key for the plaster.

• Plasterboard walls should be cleaned with a broom or brush to remove any dust. When wetting a plasterboard wall, do not use large quantities of water. A damp brush and a mix of three parts water and one part PVA adhesive brushed onto the face will control the suction.

APPLYING THE PLASTER FINISHING COAT

Applying a plaster finishing coat (also known as plaster setting) requires care and attention to detail.

1 At least 24 hours before plastering, make lime putty by soaking hydrated lime in clean water. Lime putty gives better results than hydrated lime direct from the bag.

2 Prepare the wall (see above) and scrape it down to remove any loose or projecting material. If necessary, apply a coat of cement render (see pages 8–10). Lightly scratch the wall with a metal scratcher or comb to provide a key for the plaster.

3 Wet the wall uniformly by applying water to the top of the wall and allowing it to run down the wall. This will give an indication of the amount of suction in the wall

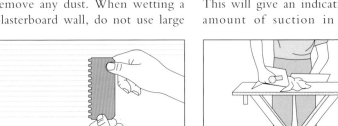

2 Lightly scratch the wall with a metal scratcher or comb to provide a key for the plaster.

5 Scrape the mixed plaster onto the plasterers hawk, ready to load your plasterers trowel.

surface. The suction should be even over the surface or the plaster will dry unevenly and crack. If it isn't even, apply a render coat.

4 Place a mixture of 60 per cent plaster and 40 per cent lime putty on a mortar board (see box on page 5). Add clean water and, with a gauging trowel, mix the materials to a workable consistency, not too stiff and not too runny. Do not overmix, or the plaster will set too fast.

5 Scrape plaster onto the plasterers' hawk, then tilt the hawk and load a plasterers trowel by scooping plaster onto the underside.

6 Apply the plaster to the wall, starting with the front of the trowel. Begin at the bottom left-hand corner of the wall, moving from left to right for a right-handed person. Quickly press the first layer firmly and thinly onto the wall. Lay the plaster evenly without ridges.

7 Using a wooden float about 450 mm long, apply a second layer of plaster. It should be slightly thicker than the first layer, about 3–4 mm thick. This layer, being heavier than the first, should cover the wall with no background showing. The two plaster layers will bond together, forming one.

8 Allow the wall to firm up. The firming process is a result of suction and the plaster starting to set. Then, using the plasterers' trowel, work over the plaster with a light, straight up-and-down action, with each long stroke overlapping the last. Trowelling compacts and flattens the surface to a hard, smooth finish. Using a brush with fine hair bristles or a fine spray, apply a little water

PLASTER BASE COAT

Another common method of plastering is a two-coat system in which a finish coat of plaster is applied over a base coat of plaster (rather than over a base coat of cement render). Different types of plaster are used for the two coats, so ask your supplier for advice.

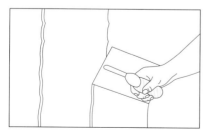

6 Starting at the bottom left-hand corner of the wall, quickly press the plaster firmly onto the surface.

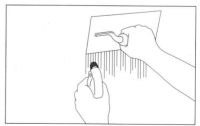

8 Apply a little water while you are trowelling, to prevent dragging and shrinkage due to moisture loss.

CORNERS

When plastering internal or external corners, use angle tools for the neatest finish. On external corners, you should secure metal corner beads to the wall before you begin to plaster. Fix the metal corner bead in place with wads of plaster or temporary nails, plaster over it and remove the nails. Don't worry if a little metal shows through, as this will be painted over.

while you are trowelling, to prevent dragging and help reduce shrinkage due to moisture loss. Trowelling should be completed as the material starts to harden and change to a darker colour. Cut a small V-joint wherever the plaster comes up against woodwork or metal frames.

PLASTERING CEILINGS

Plasterboard ceilings have now replaced traditional lath and plaster ceilings, but a concrete ceiling is sometimes plastered. If the concrete surface is very uneven, it may need a coat of cement render to level it. This should then be scratched with a metal scratcher or comb to provide a key for the finishing coat.

A concrete ceiling that is reasonably flat and level can be plastered quite simply.

1 Check the ceiling to be plastered with a straight edge and spirit level to

determine whether it can be plastered directly. Minor hollows can be filled during the plastering.

2 Clean the ceiling surface. Remove loose particles, formwork oil or algae that may be present. Wash the ceiling down if necessary.

3 If the concrete is very smooth, use a scutch hammer to hack the surface to form a key, or you may need to apply a render coat before the plaster.

4 Apply a PVA bonding agent to the surface of the ceiling, following the manufacturer's instructions.

5 If the concrete is dry, sprinkle the surface with water, and wait until the surface water has soaked in.

6 Lay on a plaster and lime finishing coat (see instructions on pages 28–9) to a thickness of not less than 2 mm.

7 Run a long, narrow timber float over the surface, filling in any hollows or blemishes. Use a steel trowel to achieve a smooth finish.

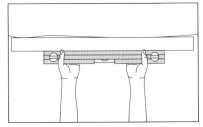

1 Check the ceiling with a straight edge and spirit level to see whether it is flat enough to be plastered directly.

PAINTING FRESH PLASTER

SEALING FRESH PLASTER

All fresh plasterwork must be sealed before the undercoat or finishing coats of paint are applied. The sealer is absorbed into the plaster surface, controlling the suction and preventing further moisture absorption. Sealers can also be used as a binding agent for chalky or powdery plaster surfaces. They ensure the finished results will look professional and be more durable.

Both oil-based (enamel) and water-based (acrylic) sealers are available. Oil-based sealers are best for wet areas, but otherwise water-based sealers are preferable, as the brushes and other equipment can be cleaned with water.

A sealer is suitable for plaster, plasterboard, cement render and masonry surfaces.

METHOD

1 Check the plaster surface and remove any loose, peeling, powdering or flaking material. Repair or fine-sand any blemishes on the surface. Ensure the plaster surface is dry and clean.

2 Apply the sealer following the manufacturer's instructions. Most water-based acrylic sealers will be touch-dry in 30 minutes on a hot, dry day of 25°C. One coat is usually enough, but if an additional coat is required it can be applied after approximately two hours. Allow longer, however, if the weather is humid or cooler.

3 Apply undercoat, if necessary, and then two coats of flat, low-sheen, satin or gloss paint as desired. Use a 100 mm flat brush for broad areas such as walls and ceilings, or a paint roller with an average width of 230 mm. Lambswool sleeves with a pile length of 10 mm are most commonly used for flat or matt emulsion paints.

PLASTER TEXTURED FINISHES

Textured finishes can be used on gypsum plaster in the same way as on cement mortar (pages 18–23).

To start with, you will need a flat base with even suction. Mix a composition mortar (see page 5) and apply it to the wall in the usual way. Allow it to dry.

Clean and wet down the base, and then apply a neat plaster coat to the area that is to be given the textured finish; ensure that no base is visible.

Spread a wetter than normal mix of plaster onto the wall and work the textured finish of your choice.

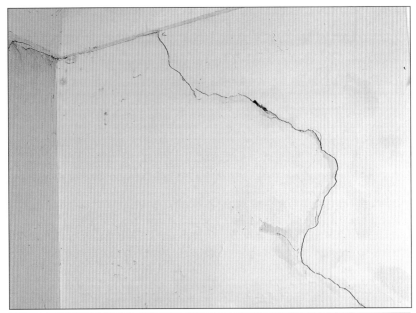

This unsightly hole (bottom) can be easily repaired with a new base coat of render and a finishing coat of plaster. The large structural crack (top), however, may need to be filled with a flexible material, as it will keep re-opening.

Repairing plaster walls

Repairing and restoring older buildings will inevitably involve repairing plasterwork. You must always use materials that are compatible with the original materials.

IDENTIFYING THE PROBLEM

Areas of plasterwork usually fail because of building movement or rising damp caused by deteriorated or non-existent damp courses. Cracks, too, are often caused by building movement, or by the use of the wrong materials, disturbance or the age of the work.

DEMOLITION AND PREPARATION

1 Protect carpet, furniture and surrounding areas by laying down plastic sheets covered with cotton dust sheets. Block off openings to prevent dust penetrating into other areas of the house.

2 Determine the extent of the area to be repaired by tapping for hollow-sounding areas. Mark a rectangular area around the faulty plaster, far enough out so that all faulty material will be removed.

3 Remove the faulty plaster and mortar by hacking it back to the brickwork over the whole marked area with a scutch hammer or chisel. Always wear a protective dust mask and eye protection when doing this.

> ### TOOLS AND MATERIALS
>
> - Mortar and plaster as required
> - Scutch hammer or chisel
> - Dust mask and eye protection
> - Paintbrushes and water brush
> - Wire brush
> - Small tool such as knife
> - Trowel, plasterers' hawk and float
> - Metal scratcher or comb

4 If the brickwork was built with lime mortar, rake out the joints to a depth of 5–10 mm as additional key for the replacement render.

5 Clean brickwork with a wire brush. Wet it to control dust.

6 Using a small tool, rake out some of the mortar behind the good plaster. Work around the hole at an angle. This will provide additional grip for the render.

PATCHING A HOLE

1 Mix the mortar (lime or composition as appropriate, see the box on page 34). An ideal ratio for lime mortar is three parts sand to one part lime. When you are ready to apply mortar to the patch, mix in

LIME AND COMPOSITION MORTARS

The plastering backgrounds in old houses usually consist of lime mortar (lime and sand) or sometimes a weak composition mortar (sand, cement and lime). Don't use cement mortar to patch a lime mortar wall or cracks will develop between the different materials, as they shrink at different rates.

Lime mortar is soft and sand-like, while cement mortar is hard, dark and difficult to remove.

some hardwall plaster to hasten the setting time. Casting plaster will help it set even faster.

2 Apply the render to the prepared background, slightly overfilling the patch. Compact the render into the patch area, and when it starts to harden, rule it off flush with the existing plaster surface.

3 Using a small tool or a trowel, scrape back the floating coat to finish 2 or 3 mm behind the original plaster finishing coat. If the patch is large, scratch the surface of the floating coat to provide grip for the new plaster finishing coat.

4 If the original or replacement render contains cement, allow another day for it to dry and for any shrinkage that may take place.

5 Keep the surface and edge of the original work clean and apply the final setting coat of plaster and lime (see pages 28–30), ensuring that the patch is trowelled flat, flush and smooth with the original surface.

REPAIRING CRAZING

Small hair-like cracks that cover the surface of the plaster are known as 'crazing'. The affected plaster should be removed and replaced.

1 If the crazing is not too severe, use a scutch hammer to gently remove the surface plaster back to the mortar.

2 If the mortar base is poor, then hack it off back to the brickwork and proceed as for patching a hole. If it is sound, damp it down using a solution of three parts water to one part PVA solution.

3 Apply a plaster finishing coat (see pages 28–30), ensuring the patch is trowelled flat, flush with the original surface and smooth.

REPAIRING FIRE CRACKING

Very fine cracks on the plaster surface are known as 'fire cracks' because they resemble the fine fire cracks in china. They can sometimes be repaired without removing the existing plaster coat.

1 If the cracking is slight, dip a fine plastic sponge or cloth into dry plaster and rub it over the fire-cracked surface in a circular motion.

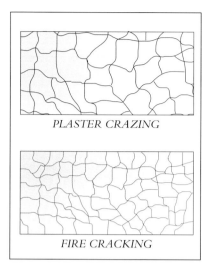

PLASTER CRAZING

FIRE CRACKING

silicon-type material. Seek advice from a hardware expert.

1 Identify the base (see the box on page 34).
• If the plaster has a lime mortar base, use a small tool, knife or scraper to widen the crack and cut back to the brickwork. Dovetail the edges behind the plaster face so as to create extra grip.
• If the mortar base is cement, use a scutch hammer, scutch chisel or a small cold chisel to widen the crack back to the brickwork. Clean out the crack using a wire brush, removing any loose material.

2 Run a wet paintbrush over the surface to provide just enough dampness so that the plaster will set in the fire cracks.

REPAIRING LARGER CRACKS

Large cracks are sometimes structural, and no matter how well or often they are repaired, they will keep opening as the building moves. You may need to treat these cracks with a flexible, non-plastering, paintable

2 Use a paint brush to wet down the crack and then apply cement-based or lime-based mortar to match the original base.

3 When the mortar is firm, cut it back with the edge of the trowel to 2–3 mm below the plaster surface and clean the area around the crack. Apply a plaster finishing coat (see pages 28–30) and trowel it to a flat, smooth finish.

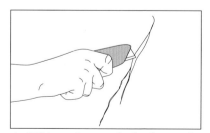

1 Widen the crack back to the brickwork, using a knife or larger tool as appropriate.

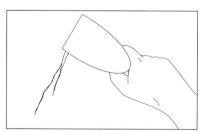

3 Cut the mortar back to 2–3 mm below the surface and apply a plaster finishing coat.

Repairing lath and plaster

Lath and plaster is a technique of plastering over long strips of soft timber nailed to timber wall studs and ceiling joists. This was a common practice throughout the nineteenth and early twentieth centuries.

REPAIRING WALLS

1 Carefully remove faulty or hollow-sounding plaster to expose the timber laths. Ensure the gap between the laths is opened up by removing any plaster keys that remain.

2 Re-nail wooden laths that are not secure and replace rusty nails, using galvanized clout or lath nails.

3 Replace any broken laths with new laths, nailing the new ones into the old positions with lath nails or galvanized clout nails. Laths were cut in lengths of 60 inches (1500 mm) and were 1½ inches (38 mm) wide. They were nailed in parallel lines, each a finger width, that is ¼ to ⅜ inch or 6–9 mm, apart. The new laths should correspond with these.

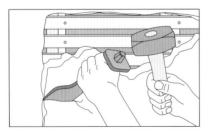

1 Using a bolster and hammer, remove faulty or hollow-sounding plaster to expose the laths.

TOOLS AND MATERIALS FOR REPAIRING WALLS

- Bolster or large chisel
- Hammer
- Lath nails or galvanized clout nails
- Laths
- Paintbrush
- PVA adhesive
- Plaster and plastering tools (see box on page 28)
- Cellulose or fibreglass strands

4 Make a key for the new plaster by making a V-shaped groove around the edges of the existing plasterwork. Carefully clean the area to be repaired with a brush and water.

5 Paint the timber laths using a paintbrush and a mix of three parts water and one part PVA adhesive to help with good bonding.

6 Replaster (see pages 28–30), pushing the first coat (the 'pricking up' coat) firmly into the gap between the wooden laths to form a firm base. Add cellulose or fibreglass strands (originally cow's hair) to the first coat to reinforce and bind the mortar.

A sagging lath and plaster ceiling can be repaired if the affected area isn't too large. There are several methods to choose from, depending on whether or not you have access to the roof cavity.

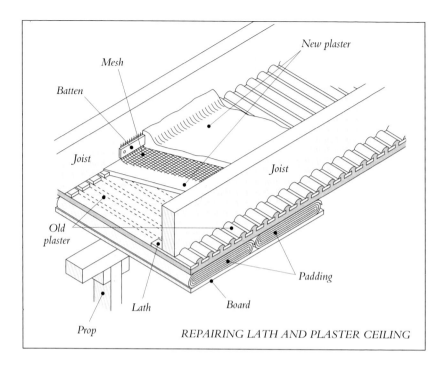

REPAIRING LATH AND PLASTER CEILING

REPAIRING CEILINGS

There are two methods for repairing sagging lath and plaster ceilings. In the first you must have access to the area above the ceiling, while for the second you work from below the ceiling. In both methods you must prop the sagging ceiling up to its original position until the plaster has set firm.

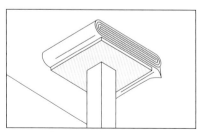

1 Prop the part of the ceiling that is sagging back to its original position using a padded board and prop.

WORKING ABOVE THE CEILING

1 Prop the part of the ceiling that is sagging back to its original position using a padded board and prop.

2 Gain access to the ceiling from above and remove rotten or broken laths and remaining nails. Clean the back of the ceiling with a vacuum cleaner and pan and brush. Old ceilings often have a very thick layer of dust and sometimes debris, so wear a dust mask.

3 Cut flymesh, chicken wire or expanded metal lath to fit between

TOOLS AND MATERIALS FOR REPAIRING CEILINGS

- Padded board and props
- Vacuum cleaner
- Hessian, chicken wire, flymesh or expanded metal lath
- Paintbrush
- PVA adhesive
- Plaster
- Bucket
- Pliers
- Timber battens, nails and hammer
- Cellulose or fibreglass strands

the joists above the damaged area. Alternatively, you can use the traditional method. Make loops of sisal or fibreglass strands and mix them with the plaster. Strap them over the ceiling joists, from one side to the other, and then fix them to the back of the ceiling. Using this method, you can omit steps 4–7.

4 Brush a solution of three parts water and one part PVA adhesive onto the cleaned ceiling area.

5 Mix neat plaster and water to a thick, pourable consistency in a bucket, and pour the mix over the top of the old plaster.

6 Fit mesh or metal lath between the joists, bedding it slightly into the poured plaster. Turn up the edges of the mesh or metal lath against the joists and secure them with timber battens nailed to the joists.

7 Apply a second coat of plaster over the top of the mesh. Allow it to set.

8 Remove the padded board and props next day and repair any superficial damage to the ceiling face.

WORKING BELOW THE CEILING
For this method you will need acrylic adhesive and gun, an electric drill, and props and a padded board.

1 Drill small holes about 100 mm apart through the sagging plaster. Do not push the drill excessively, as you may further loosen the sagging area, and do not drill into the laths.

2 Inject acrylic adhesive through the holes into and behind the ceiling.

3 Carefully push the sagging ceiling back to its original position with a padded board and prop it up until the adhesive has set.

4 Remove the prop and board. Fill the holes with plaster and give it a smooth finish.

PROPS

A board used to support the ceiling can be propped simply with a length of timber the appropriate length, or you may fix a cross-bar to the top of the prop for extra support.

Metal, adjustable props can also be hired from building supply hire firms.

Cornices, decorative plaster mouldings placed at the junction of a wall and ceiling, come in a wide variety of designs.

Installing cornices

Precast fibrous and plasterboard cornices give a neat finish to a room, covering the join between wall and ceiling. They can easily be installed by a competent handyperson.

PREPARATION

1 Take the cornice and place it in a mitre box with the wall contact edge upwards. Make sure the angled cuts (usually 45 degrees) on the ends are going in the correct direction (see the diagram opposite). Cut the pieces to length, cutting from the front of the cornice towards the back.

2 Determine how far the cornice projects from the wall. To do this, place the cornice at the base of a wall, sitting at the angle at which it will be fixed, and measure from the wall to the cornice edge. (For plasterboard cornice it will be either 55 mm or 90 mm.) On the ceiling, measure this distance from the wall.

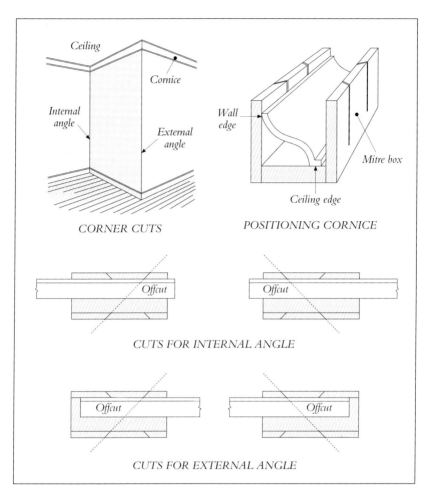

Ceiling

Cornice

Internal angle

External angle

CORNER CUTS

Wall edge

Mitre box

Ceiling edge

POSITIONING CORNICE

Offcut

Offcut

CUTS FOR INTERNAL ANGLE

Offcut

Offcut

CUTS FOR EXTERNAL ANGLE

3 Add cornice adhesive to clean water in a bucket and mix it together until it has a creamy consistency, but don't overmix it or it will set too quickly. You will need about 3 kg of adhesive for every 25 m of cornice.

FIXING THE CORNICE

4 Always fix cornice to the shortest walls in the room first. Take the

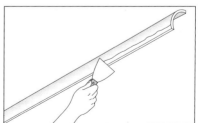

4 Using a broad knife, apply a 10 mm bead of cornice cement to the back of both edges of the cornice.

TOOLS AND MATERIALS FOR INSTALLING CORNICES

- Mitre box for 55 mm and 90 mm plaster cornice
- Handsaw
- Measuring tape and pencil
- Cornice adhesive
- Bucket
- Broad knife: 75 mm or 100 mm
- Small tool or broad knife
- Paintbrush: 100 mm
- Sponge

piece of cornice and, using a broad knife, apply a 10 mm bead of cornice cement to the back of both edges of the cornice along its full length.

5 Position the prepared cornice on the projection lines on the ceiling and press it into the angle between the wall and ceiling, firmly squeezing out excess cement. Short lengths of cornice will stay in place, but you may need to provide temporary support for longer pieces by driving nails partly into the wall and ceiling against the top and bottom edges of the cornice. If pieces of cornice must be joined for long walls, ensure that the top and bottom edges are in alignment and properly matched.

6 Spring the cornice for the longer walls into place by bowing the piece and then pushing it into position.

7 Clean off surplus cement from the cornice edges with a small tool or broad knife. Fill gaps and joints with cornice cement and smooth over the joints with a wet brush or sponge.

8 Apply a second coat of cornice cement and finish the joints with the small tool or broad knife and a wet paint brush or sponge.

9 Remove any temporary nails and fill the holes with cornice cement.

REPAIRING MOULDED CORNICES

Providing you have a section of the original cornice, you can make a plaster mould and thus reproduce the missing parts. If there are undercut parts of the cornice, however, it can only be reproduced using a gelatined rubber mould. In that case, or if you do not feel capable of making the missing pieces, a modeller can make the cornice for you. Look in your local telephone directory. There are also plaster modelling factories and outlets that specialize in decorative plasterwork. Many store a vast variety of ornate cornices that may match your original.

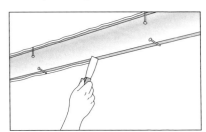

8 Apply a second coat of cornice cement and finish the joints with the small tool or broad knife.

TOOLS AND MATERIALS FOR REPAIRING CORNICES

- Timber board or plasterboard
- Shellac
- Casting plaster
- Release agent such as Vaseline
- Fibreglass strands or sisal

1 Place the piece either flat on a board or in a cradle made of timber. Make a fence around the object with timber strips, making it deep enough to prevent the wet plaster from running until it is set.

2 Apply three coats of shellac to the object and the surrounding board and fence. This provides a seal. When the shellac is dry, lightly grease it with the release agent.

3 Mix casting plaster and pour it into the fenced area to the full depth, inserting fibreglass strands in the middle. Allow it to harden.

4 Remove the plaster mould. You now have a reverse of the required

moulding. Using it, repeat steps 2–4 to create the new cornice piece.

INSTALLING A CEILING ROSE

Ceiling roses, or ceiling centres, are cast fibrous plaster mouldings used for decorative effect. A small one can be simply fixed to the ceiling, but a large one will be heavy and you should support the ceiling by screwing timber battens to the back of the ceiling above where the rose will be.

1 Find the centre of the ceiling by stretching string or chalk lines from the corners of the room to form diagonal, intersecting lines.

2 With a small tool, roughen up the back of the rose, carving criss-cross lines for extra grip. Thoroughly wet the back of the rose with a brush and water to reduce suction.

3 Mix cornice adhesive and water to a creamy consistency. Using a notched trowel, spread adhesive over the back of the rose and press the rose firmly into position. Support it with a padded board and prop.

4 Cut away excess adhesive from the edges of the rose, fill any voids and smooth the edges with a small tool and wet sponge. Allow the adhesive to set and remove the prop.

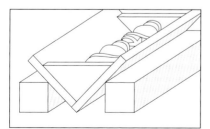

1 Make a fence around the piece with timber strips, making it deep enough to hold the wet plaster.

Types of plasterboard

Most modern houses are lined with plasterboard. This alternative to traditional plastering, known as dry-lining, can be successfully installed by the amateur.

TYPES OF PLASTERBOARD

Plasterboard is a machine-made sheet that has a core of fire-resistant gypsum plaster encased in heavy-duty paper lining. It comes in a number of different forms, each of which has specific uses. Sheet lengths usually start at 1.2 m.

TAPERED-EDGE

Tapered-edge plasterboard is the standard plasterboard used for most applications. The long edges of the board are tapered. When joined to other sheets, they form a shallow channel that is filled with plaster-based bedding cement and paper tape to make a smooth, continuous surface. The sheets are 10, 13, 15 or 19 mm thick and 600 to 1200 mm wide.

SQUARE-EDGE BASEBOARD

Mouldings of timber, vinyl or aluminium are used to cover the joints of square-edge baseboard, or the sheets can simply be butted together. These sheets are 10 or 13 mm thick and 900 mm wide.

FIRE-RATED

This plasterboard is manufactured with a recessed joint for flush finishing, but it has a reinforced mineral core that has additional resistance to fire. Gypsum plaster is a natural fire-resistant material, and consequently, the thicker the board, the greater the fire resistance. Fire-rated board has a pink lining. Sheets 13 or 16 mm thick are 1200 mm wide, while 25 mm board (used for commercial applications as a shaft wall liner) is 600 mm wide.

WATER-RESISTANT

Water-resistant plasterboard is a recessed-edge board with green paper lining. The core, face and back of the sheet are treated to make it resistant to moisture and humidity. It is designed specifically to be used in bathrooms, laundries, kitchens, toilets or any area exposed to moisture. Sheets 10 mm thick are 1200 or 1350 mm wide; 13 mm thick sheet is 1200 mm wide.

LIGHTWEIGHT CEILING

You can use 13 mm standard plasterboard for ceiling sheets (the thinner 10 mm board tends to sag), but the supporting joists must be no more than 450 mm apart. However, stronger, lighter sheets specifically designed for ceilings are also manufactured. They will span

Bottom to top: pink-lined fire-rated board; standard tapered-edge board; green-lined water-resistant board; ceiling panel; and lightweight ceiling board.

600 mm between joists and so there is a saving in the number and size of joists required. They also require less effort to install. This board is 10 mm thick and comes in widths of 1200 mm or 1350 mm.

FOIL-BACKED

Foil-backed plasterboard is standard recessed-edge plasterboard that has a layer of aluminium foil laminated to the back to provide extra insulation. However, if over time a thick layer of dust settles on the back of the board, the special insulating qualities are reduced. It is available in the same thicknesses, widths and lengths as standard plasterboard.

CEILING PANELS

These are infill panels used for some suspended ceiling systems. They are made from standard plasterboard with square edges, and the surface may be plain, factory painted in matt white, vinyl laminated or have a poly-coated paper laminated to the surface. Panels are 13 mm thick with a nominal size of 600 x 1200 mm.

FIBRE-CEMENT BOARD

Fibre-cement board is a cement-based product that is used as an alternative to plasterboard. It offers high resistance to moisture, is non-combustible and has higher impact resistance than plasterboard.

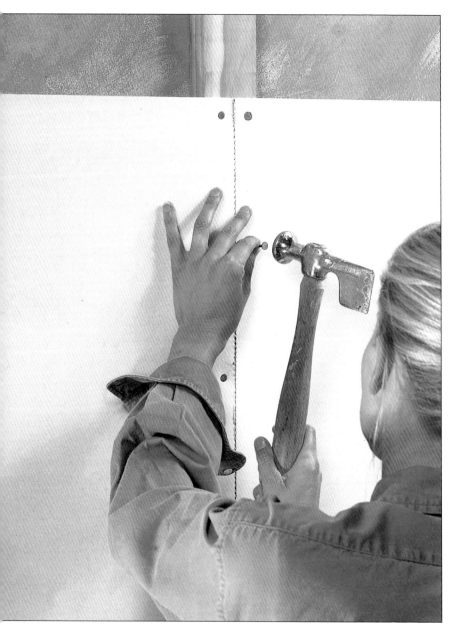

A wallboard hammer is used to nail through plasterboard without breaking the paper liner. The rounded face creates a dimple that will later be covered with bedding and skimming plaster.

Installing plasterboard

Plasterboard is an easy-to-install lining for interior walls and ceilings. It is easy to cut and can be fixed to the house frame in a number of ways.

MEASURING AND ORDERING

First decide which type of plasterboard you will need (see pages 44–5). In particular, remember that in wet areas such as kitchens, bathrooms and laundries you should use water-resistant plasterboard or fibre-cement sheeting. If you are using standard board, use 10 mm for walls and 13 mm (or lightweight ceiling board) for ceilings.

There are two ways to calculate how many sheets you will need. Either measure each ceiling and wall frame, list them and work out the sheets to suit each frame, or order enough of one sheet size (for example, 2400 x 1200 mm) to cover all frames. This makes ordering easier, but there will be more cutting and you may have to buy extra sheets.

TOOLS AND MATERIALS

- Measuring tape: 5 m or 8 m
- Carpenters pencil
- Utility or trimming knife
- Handsaw
- Wallboard hammer or screw gun and Phillips-head bit
- Nails or screws (see page 48)
- Broad knife: 25 mm
- Acrylic stud adhesive
- Casing bead
- Cornice cement, battens and notched trowel (if back-blocking)

STORING

Always handle and carry plasterboard sheets on edge (upright). They may break if you carry them flat.

When plasterboard sheets are delivered, stack them flat, face to face

Always carry plasterboard sheets on edge (upright) as they may break if you carry them flat.

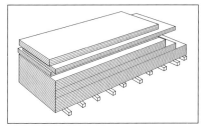

Store plasterboard sheets flat, face to face and supported on level bearers placed no more than 600 mm apart.

and in a dry area. Support them on level bearers placed no more than 600 mm apart and 150 mm in from the ends. Stack ceiling sheets separately or on top of the stack, as ceilings are installed before walls.

When you need to use the sheets, lift them off the stack. Never drag them off, or they may fracture.

CUTTING PLASTERBOARD

Plasterboard is very easy to cut. All you need is a utility knife and guide.

1 On the front of the plasterboard sheet, measure and mark the required length using a tape, straight edge and pencil. Mark the board lightly, as heavy pencil lines may show through paint. Using a straight edge as a guide, score along the line with a utility knife.

2 Snap the sheet along the cut to break it. The sheet will still be held together by the back liner.

3 Bend the board and run the knife along the back liner at an angle so that it cuts along the same line.

CHOOSING FIXINGS

The fixings you use are partly dependent on the type of wall.

• Timber framing. You can fix plasterboard to timber framing using galvanized plasterboard nails or self-tapping screws, or a combination of acrylic stud adhesive and either nails or screws. This is the best choice. If you don't use adhesive, double-nail the sheets, that is, place the nails 50–65 mm apart, as this provides closer contact between the board and the frame. Always use a wallboard hammer, as it makes a dimpled depression when you drive home the nail – a claw hammer will damage the board.

• Metal framing. Screws and a power screwdriver are used to fix plasterboard to metal framing. Use a type S needle or drill point, self-drilling or self-tapping screws.

• Masonry walls. Plasterboard can be fixed directly to brick, stone or concrete block walls using masonry adhesive, or timber battens can be screwed to the walls and then the sheets fixed to the battens as for timber framing.

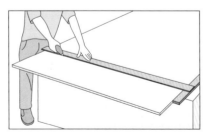

1 Lightly mark the board and then, using a straight edge as a guide, score along the line with a utility knife.

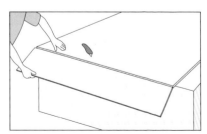

2 Snap the sheet along the cut to break it – the sheet will be held together by the back liner.

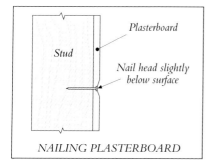

NAILING PLASTERBOARD

USING NAILS

1 Take the wallboard hammer, holding it at the end of the handle, and hold the nail in your other hand, between the index finger and thumb. The shank of the nail should be at right angles to the board.

2 Drive the nail through the plasterboard and into the timber frame using short, firm strokes. Once the nail is embedded in the board and will support itself, let your hand fall away and continue hammering until the head of the nail is flush with the plasterboard. Then give one more controlled blow to drive it below the surface. The nail head must be slightly below the surface of

1 Hold the hammer at the end of the handle and the nail between index finger and thumb of your other hand.

the plasterboard, but take care not to tear the paper liner.

3 Check that all the nails are slightly below the surface by running a broad knife across the face of the board over each nail head. A metallic-sounding scrape will tell you the nail needs to be driven in further.

USING SCREWS

1 Insert a Phillips-head bit into the power screwdriver. Tighten the bit in the centre of the chuck. Magnetic bits make positioning and holding the screws easier.

2 Adjust the clutch of the screwdriver to determine how far the screw will penetrate the plasterboard.

3 Drive the screws into the board, ensuring the head is just below the surface of the board, as when nailing.

USING ACRYLIC STUD ADHESIVE

Using stud adhesive reduces the number of nails or screws needed and, therefore, reduces the amount of nail stopping and sanding. The adhesive is water-based and has a thick, creamy consistency so that it is easy to apply and clean up.

Don't apply adhesive at butt joints, at internal and external angles or on sheet edges. Never apply adhesive at the same location as a nail or screw. When the adhesive sets, it shrinks and draws the board towards the frame. This will cause the finishing plaster over the nail head or screw to crack as the board moves away from the rigid nail or screw.

1 Apply dabs of adhesive to the frame with a 25 mm broad knife. Each dab should be about 25 mm in diameter and 15 mm thick. For a 900 mm wide sheet you should use three dabs, for a 1200 mm wide sheet four dabs and for a 1350 mm wide sheet five dabs.

2 Place one end of the sheet in place and swing the sheet against the framing like a hinge.

3 Nail or screw the bottom of the sheet to each stud, between 10 and 16 mm from the edge of the board.

4 Fix plasterboard offcuts against the sheet at every second stud to hold it in place for a minimum of 24 hours, until the adhesive has set.

5 Nail the sheet ends to the frame at 200 mm centres, except in angles and around door and window openings when you should use 300 mm centres. If you are using screw fixings, place the screws at 300 mm centres in all situations.

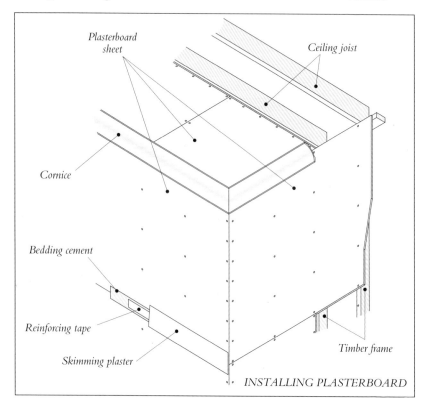

Plasterboard sheet

Ceiling joist

Cornice

Bedding cement

Reinforcing tape

Skimming plaster

Timber frame

INSTALLING PLASTERBOARD

INSTALLING CEILINGS

Ceiling sheets are usually installed before wall sheets. They should be fixed at right angles to the framing members for more strength and to prevent sagging. Two people are needed to fix ceiling sheets.

1 Prepare scaffolding in the room. The scaffold should be set so that the distance from the ceiling joists to the scaffold is the same as your height. When the plasterboard is held in position, it then rests on your head.

2 Measure and cut the plasterboard to length (see page 48). If you need to join sheets, butt the ends together and ensure the join is centred under a ceiling joist or batten. Alternatively, the join can fall centrally between members and be back-blocked (see box on page 62). If there is access to the space above the ceiling, the sheets may be fixed before the back blocks are applied. In rooms more than one sheet long, the longest sheet is fixed against one wall, then the next sheet against the wall at the other end of the ceiling and, finally, the shorter infill sheets. The sheets should fit tight against the wall if you will not be adding cornices, but if you are using cornices, the sheets can stop short (see the box on page 53).

3 Measure the ceiling width and cut the sheets to fit if necessary.

4 Determine your method of fixing (see page 48). Ceiling sheets have an

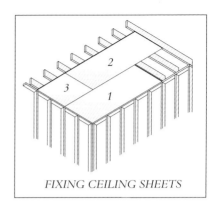

FIXING CEILING SHEETS

extra row of double nailing or screws up the centre of the sheet at the point of intersection with the framing. The nails are spaced 50–75 mm apart. If you are using stud adhesive, use two dabs for 900 mm wide sheets and four dabs for sheets 1200 or 1350 mm wide.

5 With both people standing on the scaffold, lift the first sheet above your heads. Hold the sheet in its final position, hard up to the underside of the framing.

6 While your helper continues to hold the sheet firm, support it on

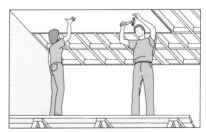

6 While your helper holds the sheet firm, support it on your head and fix one end to the framing.

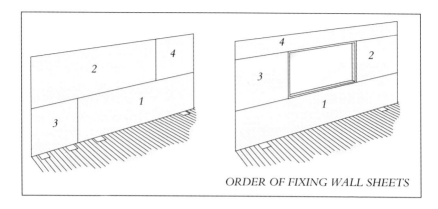

ORDER OF FIXING WALL SHEETS

your head and fix one end of the sheet to the framing. Then fix the other end of the sheet in the same manner. Finally, both of you combine to fix the sides.

INSTALLING WALLS

Plasterboard is fixed to the walls after the ceiling sheets are in place. Always install the sheets at right angles to the framing (horizontally), as there are fewer joints and the sheets can bridge irregularities in the framing members. This also provides greater strength and keeps cracking of the joints to a minimum. Position butt joints in the centre of frame studs or joists, or back-block them, and fix the sheets 10 mm off the floor to avoid joints cracking as the frame moves.

Butt wall sheets tightly up against the ceiling if you are not using cornices. If you are installing cornices, the cornice must overlap the wall sheet by at least 25 mm (see the box opposite).

Splitting sheets above and below window openings can sometimes minimize wastage. However, avoid joints over door openings as the joint will be subject to stresses and may crack if the door tends to slam shut.

1 Check the frame and flashing and make any necessary repairs. Also check the locations of electrical and plumbing installations so you can avoid them when fixing the sheets.

2 Measure and cut the sheets (see page 48). For walls longer than one sheet, position the longest sheet at one end of the bottom row, with the longest sheet for the top half of the wall at the opposite end of the wall. The shorter sections are placed in between, with the joints staggered at least one framing member apart.

3 Make offcuts from 10 mm board for packers below the sheets. Place them in position along the frame where they will support the sheets.

4 Cut lengths of casing bead as necessary (see the box on page 57). It

is fixed in place as you install the plasterboard sheets.

5 If you are using stud adhesive, apply it to the frame where the first sheet (the longest sheet on the bottom row) will be fixed. Place one end of the plasterboard sheet into the internal angle of the walls and swing it (hinge-fashion) into position. Fix the sheet as required (see page 48).

6 Apply stud adhesive (if applicable) to the frame and then position the upper sheet so that it rests on the recessed edge of the bottom sheet, bringing it into position hinge-fashion as before. Fix the board.

7 When the wall contains window or door openings, you can fix the sheet in place across the opening if necessary. Using a handsaw, saw underhand up to the frame head (or downwards as applicable) on each side of the opening. Then, using the utility knife, score across the opening and bend the board to snap it. Finish by scoring across the back of the sheet and removing the piece of board.

FIXING CORNICES TO PLASTERBOARD

Cornices can be fixed in place at any stage after the ceiling and wall sheets are installed and before the final finishing coat is applied to the joints.

The cornice must overlap the ceiling and wall sheets by at least 25 mm. It is fixed in place with cornice adhesive in the same way as cornice added to plastered walls (see pages 40–3). As always, be careful to make correctly angled cuts for the corners.

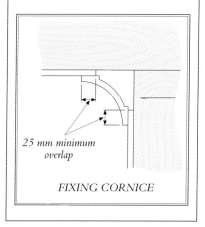

25 mm minimum overlap

FIXING CORNICE

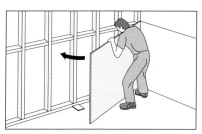

5 Place one end of the sheet into the internal angle of the walls and swing it (hinge-fashion) into position.

6 Position the upper sheet on the bottom sheeting, bringing it into position hinge-fashion.

Finishing plasterboard

The techniques used to finish the joints and corners of plasterboard are crucial to achieving a professional-looking result. Investing in the correct tools for each stage will be worthwhile.

TOOLS AND MATERIALS

- Bedding cement
- Reinforcing tape
- Skimming plaster
- Mixing bucket
- Plasterers' hawk
- Broad knife: 100 mm and 150 mm
- Offset broad knife: 75 mm
- Curved trowel: 200 mm and 275 mm
- Straight trowel: 275 mm
- Internal angle tool
- External angle tool (optional)
- External angle bead
- Flat paintbrush: 100 mm
- Sanding float
- Abrasive paper (150 grit) or mesh (220 grit)

THREE-COAT SYSTEM

After you have fixed the plasterboard to the frame, you have to cover the joints, edges, corners and nail heads with cement in order to hide them and provide a smooth finish for paint. The three-coat system will give you the best finish, and the one best able to resist cracking if climatic changes and unstable foundation soils apply stresses to the building frames.

The first or base coat consists of bedding cement and reinforcing tape, the second coat is bedding cement, and the third consists of skimming (or finishing) plaster or compound.

Bedding cement is a plaster-based cement that has low-shrinkage properties and is available in various setting times. Allow at least 75 minutes between coats. Bedding cement provides the strongest joints, although it is a little harder to use than topping cement. It is available in bag sizes from 2.5 kg to 20 kg.

Perforated paper tape is the strongest tape available and it will give the best results, but fibreglass self-adhesive tape is also available and is easy to use.

Skimming plaster is available as a ready-mixed material in plastic buckets or as a dry powder that must be mixed with water. The ready-mixed version is the most popular. These cements will shrink and

HINT

If there are any gaps between your plasterboard sheets, fill them with cement and allow it to set hard before you begin the finishing process.

When plasterboard is finished correctly, the joints will be completely hidden.
To match existing corners in an older part of the house, the corners here are
finished with the staff beads used in traditional plastering.

TOOLS FOR PLASTERBOARD

Specialist plasterers will use a variety of tools and materials when they are working with plasterboard. However, you will be able to achieve a good result using only the tools and materials listed on pages 47 and 54, all of which are readily available.

harden as the water they contain evaporates. Leave them to dry for 24 hours before finishing with a sanding float and abrasive paper.

Bedding cements and skimming plasters should be treated in the same way as other gypsum plasters:
• Don't remix cement, and don't add water to a previous mix of cement.
• Don't continue to use cement after the initial set has taken place.
• Store cement in a dry location.
• Don't mix different cements together or with other materials.

RECESSED JOINTS
1 Mix bedding cement with clean water in a bucket and, with a pointing trowel, transfer it to a plasterers' hawk. Using a 150 mm broad knife, apply it to the recess. Hold the knife with two fingers on the blade. First make short strokes across the joint, and then a long sweeping stroke along the length of the joint.

2 Place tape in the centre of the joint and apply pressure with the broad knife to bed it into the cement. Work the full length of the joint.

3 Using the remaining mixed cement, apply a thin coat over the tape and joint. Allow it to set hard.

4 Mix a second coat of bedding cement and apply it to the joint using a 200 mm curved trowel. First use short strokes across the joint, and then a long sweeping stroke along the joint. Allow the cement to set hard.

5 Using a 275 mm curved trowel, apply a third, finishing coat of ready-mixed skimming plaster to the recess, using short strokes across the joint and then a long one along the joint.

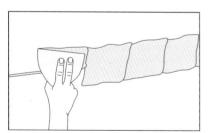

1 Use a 150 mm broad knife to apply bedding cement to the recess, making short strokes across the joint.

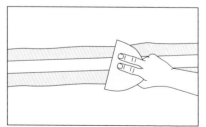

2 Place tape on the centre of the joint and apply pressure with the broad knife to bed it into the cement.

FINISHING EDGES

Whenever plasterboard butts up to another material, such as brickwork or timber, cover the edges of the sheet with casing bead, a metal or vinyl beading that protects the plasterboard. It also makes a neat edge around windows and door jambs. Casing bead is fixed in place as you install the sheets.

On external corners use external angle bead, a metal beading that allows you to make a smooth, straight corner. It is fixed on at the beginning of the finishing process.

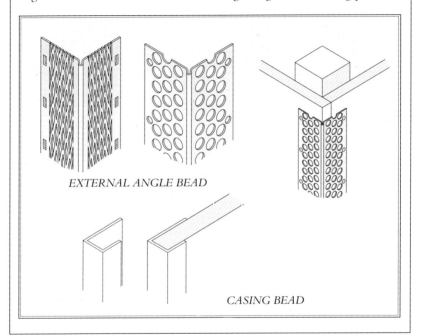

EXTERNAL ANGLE BEAD

CASING BEAD

6 Dampen a brush with water and use it to soften and feather the edges of the cement for the full length of the joint.

7 Allow the cement to dry for approximately 24 hours, and then sand the joint smooth using a sanding float with 150 grit abrasive paper or 220 grit mesh.

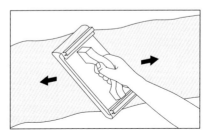

7 Allow the cement to dry and sand the joint smooth, using a sanding float with abrasive paper or mesh.

BUTT JOINTS

Butt joints will finish above the surface of the plasterboard as the tape and cement are placed on the surface of the board.

1 Mix and apply bedding cement to either side of the joint, using a 150 mm broad knife.

2 Place the tape in the centre of the joint and, applying pressure with the broad knife, bed it into the cement for the full length of the joint.

3 Using the remaining mixed cement, apply a thin coat over the face of the tape and joint. Allow the cement to set hard.

4 Mix a second coat of bedding cement and apply it to either side of the joint, using a 275 mm straight trowel so that the cement extends about three-quarters the length of the trowel either side of the centre of the joint.

5 Using the straight trowel, apply a third, finishing coat of ready-mixed skimming plaster. The finished width of the joint should be equal to the full length of the trowel either side of the centre of the joint.

6 Dampen a brush with water and use it to soften and feather the edges of the cement for the full length of the joint.

7 Sand the joint smooth, using a sanding float with 150 grit abrasive paper or 220 grit mesh, so that it finishes with a slight convex camber.

INTERNAL CORNERS

Internal corners are finished in the same way as other joints, using reinforcing tape, but with an internal angle tool.

1 Mix and apply bedding cement to either side of the internal corner, using a 75 mm offset broad knife. The cement will cover an area 75 mm wide on each wall.

2 Cut the reinforcing tape to the required length and fold it down the centre. Bed the tape into the cement.

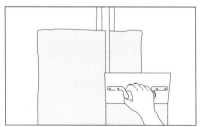

5 Using the straight trowel, apply a third, finishing coat of ready-mixed skimming plaster to the butt joint.

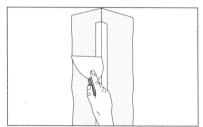

2 Cut the tape to the required length, fold it down the centre and bed it into the cement in the internal corner.

3 Apply a thin coat of cement over the face of the tape and joint and allow it to set hard.

4 Using a 100 mm broad knife, apply a second coat of ready-mixed skimming plaster to either side of the corner. Pass an internal angle finishing tool down the corner, starting from the top and keeping the tool fairly flat. Place your fingers on either edge of the tool and press to help feather the edges.

5 Use a damp brush to feather the edges as previously described.

6 Sand to a smooth finish with a sanding float, using long, firm strokes up and down both sides of the corner.

EXTERNAL CORNERS

External corners are finished using external angle bead (see the box on page 57) to protect the corners from impact damage. You can complete the job using a normal broad knife and straight trowel or you can use a special external angle tool for the final coat.

1 Fix external angle bead over the corner so that it is straight and does not protrude from the wall.

2 Mix and apply bedding cement to either side of the angle bead, using a 150 mm broad knife. Press one side of the broad knife against the apex of the bead while pressing the other side against the plasterboard face, at the same time feathering the edge with pressure. Allow the cement to set hard.

3 Mix and apply a second coat of bedding cement to either side of the corner, using a 275 mm straight trowel. The cement width either side of the apex should be approximately three-quarters the length of the trowel. Allow the cement to set hard.

4 Apply a third, finishing coat of ready-mixed skimming plaster to either side of the corner, working to a width equal to the full length of the straight trowel.

5 Feather the edges and sand in the usual manner.

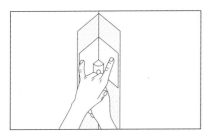

4 Pass an internal angle tool down the corner, starting from the top and keeping the tool fairly flat.

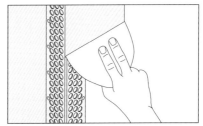

2 Apply cement, pressing one side of the knife against the apex of the bead and the other against the board.

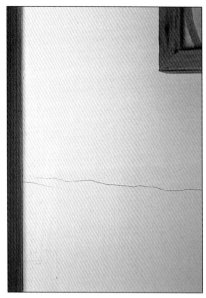

Cracks in plasterboard joints (left) are best repaired by cleaning them out and refinishing, while the damaged plasterboard around the hole (right) can be cut away and replaced.

Repairing plasterboard

Plasterboard can be easily damaged with hard or sharp objects, but it is not difficult to repair, although you will need basic plasterboard installation and finishing equipment.

CRACKS

Cracks may appear in plasterboard if there is structural movement in the building. They are easy to repair.

Using a sharp knife, cut out a V-shape along the length of the crack. Scrape away loose material and clean the board with a brush.

Mix cornice adhesive and, using a broad knife, fill the crack flush with the surrounding surface. Apply a thin layer of ready-mixed skimming plaster and sand smooth and flush.

Cracks may also occur along joints between plasterboard sheets if the joints were not originally finished correctly with good-quality reinforcing tape and cement. Clean the joints out and finish the joints as described on pages 54–9.

HOLES

Small holes and dents can be treated in the same way as cracks. There are several ways to repair larger holes.

METHOD 1

1 Cut a piece of plasterboard in a square or rectangular shape a little larger than the hole to be repaired. Place the piece of board on the wall over the hole and trace around it.

2 Remove the piece of board and mark diagonal lines from the corners of the shape to the centre. Use a handsaw to cut along each diagonal line from the hole to the corner.

3 With a trimming knife and straight edge, cut the plasterboard liner along the outline. Bend and cut away the pieces inside the outline.

4 Cut two small blocks from plasterboard. Mix cornice adhesive and apply it to the blocks, positioning them behind the hole on the inside surface of the wall but half exposed. Allow at least an hour for the cement to set hard.

REPAIRING SMALL HOLES

1 Cut a piece of plasterboard a similar width but slightly longer than the hole to be repaired.

2 Make a small hole through the piece of board and thread string or wire through it. Tie the string to a nail at the back of the board.

3 Mix enough cornice adhesive to cover the edges of the hole.

4 Slide the piece of board into the hole and pull it tight with the string. While holding it tight, apply cornice cement to the edges of the hole. Allow the cement to set and cut off the string.

5 Fill the hole with cement, allow it to dry and sand the area smooth to the existing surface.

---

5 Fix the piece of plasterboard cut in step 1 to the exposed blocks with cornice cement and tape. Set the joints in the normal manner.

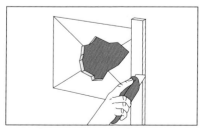

3 With a trimming knife and straight edge, cut the plasterboard liner along the outline.

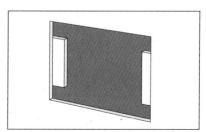

4 Mix cornice cement and apply it to the blocks, positioning them behind the hole but half-exposed.

BACK-BLOCKING

Plasterboard joints that fall between framing members are back-blocked. This involves fitting pieces of plasterboard between the studs and then fixing the wall sheets to them with cornice cement.

1 Cut pieces of plasterboard at least 250 mm long and wide enough to fit between the studs. These are the back-blocking pieces.

2 Nail timber battens or strips of plasterboard to the sides of the studs so that they are set back about 18 mm from the face of the stud.

3 Hold a back-blocking piece against the battens and screw or nail it to the studs.

4 With a notched trowel or spreader, apply beads of cornice cement horizontally over the face of the back block.

5 Fix the plasterboard wall sheets in place so that the joint will be within 50 mm of the centre line

between the studs. Nail a small piece of plasterboard into the stud through the plasterboard sheet to hold it in position until the adhesive dries.

6 Fix a packing strip over the joint and hold it in position with horizontal battens nailed into the studs. Leave the nails protruding so that they can be removed later.

7 Allow the cornice cement to set hard, and then remove the battens and packing strips. There should now be a depression about 3 mm deep along the joint. Tape and set the joint as usual.

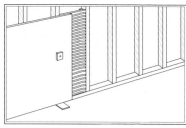

5 Fix the sheets in place so the joint will be within 50 mm of the centre line of the studs.

METHOD 2
For a more complete repair, you can replace a whole section of damaged plasterboard. This is also a less fiddly, more straightforward job.

1 Cut the plasterboard around the hole back to the nearest studs.

2 Cut a new piece of plasterboard that will exactly match the size of the board you have cut away.

3 Install the piece of plasterboard as for new plasterboard (see pages 46–53) and finish the joints as appropriate (see pages 54–9).

Tools for plastering and rendering

Some of the most useful tools for plastering and rendering are shown below. Build up your tool kit gradually – most of the tools can be purchased from your local hardware or DIY store.

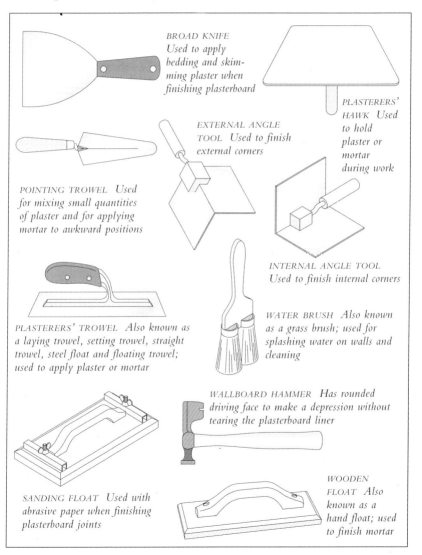

BROAD KNIFE Used to apply bedding and skimming plaster when finishing plasterboard

PLASTERERS' HAWK Used to hold plaster or mortar during work

EXTERNAL ANGLE TOOL Used to finish external corners

POINTING TROWEL Used for mixing small quantities of plaster and for applying mortar to awkward positions

INTERNAL ANGLE TOOL Used to finish internal corners

PLASTERERS' TROWEL Also known as a laying trowel, setting trowel, straight trowel, steel float and floating trowel; used to apply plaster or mortar

WATER BRUSH Also known as a grass brush; used for splashing water on walls and cleaning

WALLBOARD HAMMER Has rounded driving face to make a depression without tearing the plasterboard liner

SANDING FLOAT Used with abrasive paper when finishing plasterboard joints

WOODEN FLOAT Also known as a hand float; used to finish mortar

Index